Breast Cancer Conquered Together

A Journey of Hope

Breast Cancer Conquered Together

DENISE COATES

Matador
Unit E2 Airfield Business Park,
Harrison Road, Market Harborough,
Leicestershire. LE16 7UL
Tel: 0116 2792299
Email: books@troubador.co.uk
Web: www.troubador.co.uk/matador
Twitter: @matadorbooks

ISBN 978 1805141 815

British Library Cataloguing in Publication Data.
A catalogue record for this book is available from the British Library.

Printed and bound in Great Britain by 4edge Limited
Typeset in 11pt Minion Pro by Troubador Publishing Ltd, Leicester, UK

Matador is an imprint of Troubador Publishing Ltd

For, Dr Ruth James,

"You gave me hope and through that I found my courage"

For all of us who face this challenge we can come together as a united front and support one another and give hope for our future generations.

*"I am not what happened to me,
I'm what I choose to become."*

About Me

I'm Denise Coates, and on the 24th of December 2015, I heard these words:

> *"Denise, there is an eighty per cent*
> *chance you have breast cancer."*

So, looking up at the clock, I knew that my life would be different. How different, I didn't know; was that it?

This is a combination of my story and what I learnt through this journey. It's also about what helped me and how my life changed in the aftermath of my breast cancer experience.

It's about hope, it's about awareness of early detection and with the support of like-minded inspirational women, including a male breast cancer survivor who have shared their survival stories and tips. It's about the gratitude and appreciation of life and giving back.

Like the uniqueness of cancer, we all have our own ways of dealing with this type of experience! It reminds me of the old saying: 'One shoe size doesn't fit all'.

Mine is to give back and to create awareness and for people to feel hopeful.

My wish would be that somewhere in this story you find something that will help in some way. Or indeed, if someone you know is going through cancer, it may help them too.

Thank you!

Acknowledgements

Dr Ruth James and the Breast Cancer Unit, the MDT *(Multi-Disciplinary Team)* including Jan and the breast screening team at our NHS, L&D Hospital, Luton.

The RH Andrew Selous, Conservative MP for Southwest Bedfordshire.

Challney High School for Girls, particularly Nic Ponsonby.

Support from breast cancer groups, Dr Lisa Schwartz, Andrea, Helen, Karen, Pat and Susan, Sue, and Sally Ann.

Journalists: Liz Summers, ITV Anglia, and Holly Patel, *Luton Today*.

To *all* the women out there who support one another through breast cancer globally.

Family, Pete, Jamie, Steve, Robin, Alison, Heather and all my friends.

I thank you.

Contents

What Cancer Means to Me   1

Time   4

Going Public #Awareness   7

Exercise   11

Screening and Breast Cancer   17

Family and Friends… Yes, You Have Cancer!   22

Treatment Plan   26

Operation Day 4th February 2016, World Cancer Day!   30

Don't Be So Hard on Yourself   35

New Normal Life   41

Survivor Stories   45

Survivors' Tips   54

Cancer and Mental Health – CBT   57

Research and Hope   59

Recurrence   62

Giving Back   66

ABS – International Projects Fundraising   69

Awareness and Education   72

My Talk at Dunstable Downs   78

What Cancer Means to Me

Every cancer experience is unique to the patient. This is my story, and my way of saying 'thank you' to all the amazing professionals who've taken such great care of me.

On World Cancer Day, I want to tell you what it means to me in the hope that I can inspire more people into action.

*

World Cancer Day will always be a significant day for me…

Why? Well, my first operation to remove my breast tumours fell on that day, Thursday 4th February 2016. I remember thinking to myself, of all days, my op had to be on this day!

On reflection it was a good thing because, as a Cancer Research UK media representative, I managed to place an article on the Race for Life website, as I was preparing myself to tackle their 5K after my treatment was finished, which I did three days after my radiotherapy. I felt very proud when I completed the 5K, and I also had the opportunity to talk to 1,000 women on stage about my experience, encouraging early detection and breast cancer awareness. On the day of my operation, I saw my update appear on their page, and all the messages of love and support along with hope all started to flood in, which really spurred me on.

My tumours, albeit small, were in the left quadrant of my breast, and the surgeon who worked with me discussed my options. I decided on a breast mammoplasty reduction-style surgery and was extremely delighted with the result, but most importantly the margins were clear of cancer. On 19th January 2017 I had symmetrising surgery on my right breast.

I have been treated at the Luton and Dunstable Hospital Breast Cancer Unit and was so impressed with the overall care and multi-disciplinary team approach, which consists of your own dedicated breast care nurse, surgeon, oncologist, radiologist, and pathologist, not forgetting the ward nurses. My dream teams.

Another NHS establishment that was part of my overall treatment plan – twenty-one days of radiotherapy – was at the Mount Vernon Cancer Centre. My time here was a real awakening for me. I was collected every day by a contracted hospital taxi firm, and they certainly brightened up my day! Very caring, thoughtful, and funny gentlemen – they made such a difference, which really did brighten up each day.

Whilst at Mount Vernon I had time to process my cancer experience, and an overwhelming feeling of gratitude and life-affirming feelings grasped me. I met incredible staff and women, and I have to say, it has changed my outlook on life! I saw humility and kindness beyond measure, something I will not forget in a hurry.

I remember watching a clip-on YouTube of Lisa Schwartz, MD, MBA. She says:

"I think the triumph is defined by the patient, because there are some patients that will go through their treatment and they will have been so changed by that treatment emotionally, that they'll

go back on and give back to the community, inspired by the lessons they've learnt and for them that's their triumph!"

Well, this is my story of triumph, and my way of saying a massive 'thank you' to the L&D breast cancer 'team' and to our wonderful NHS along with family and friends.

Time

Let's face it, we are mainly unprepared for this scenario – it's not going to happen to me, is it?

Well, unfortunately statistics say that one in two or three of us will get cancer!

I can recall the events of the diagnosis day as if it was yesterday. Why? Because it kicked my conscious mind into action. I believe up to that point, I was just running on autopilot.

Sitting opposite the doctor, who delivered the message, "Denise there is an eighty per cent chance you have breast cancer," will stay with me for some time and I distinctly remember looking at the clock on the wall and thinking, *Denise! that clock is* not stopping... you are now up against time.

So, with my conscious mind woken up, I talked myself into what I can only describe as self-preservation goals. I decided to limit my thoughts about my outcome – why worry about something that was out of my control?

I soon realised that anxiety and thinking negatively would hinder my chances of survival, so I made more conscious decisions to try and take an integrated approach.

Eat – *good nutritious food.*
Exercise – *Pilates, jogging.*
Drink – *keep hydrated, mainly water.*
Laugh – *try and have some fun.*

Remain as determined and positive as I could be.

I tackled the cancer dilemma head on with the support and medical help from the L&D Hospital, NHS, multi-disciplinary breast cancer medical team… My dream team, particularly, Dr Ruth James.

Looking back, I realised the small amount of CBT training I'd had some years before really helped, changing my thought processes and being mindful that my behaviours would either help or hinder my outcome.

Quite a bit of time has passed, and I've been on a path of self-development, needing to adjust and make changes to my new normal life!

I have changed jobs and achieved some rather significant milestones. I've campaigned for cancer awareness in education and now I'm voluntarily fundraising with the Association of Breast Surgery on an international project. I am conducting awareness and motivational workshops and talks, promoting that all-important message of early detection.

Here I am at London's Luton Airport...

Thank you for taking your 'time' to read this. I hope it helps!

Going Public

#Awareness

Read all about it!

Right from the get-go, I decided to use my social media platforms as a voice about awareness of early detection of breast cancer, reminding people to go for screenings and get checked out sooner rather than later.

I consciously decided this after my family and friends were informed of my breast cancer.

Here is my first post. The response was overwhelming, and I really did feel the love and good wishes that were bestowed upon me.

13th January 2016

Hot off the press! Health news alert! unfortunately, I have breast cancer.

This post is to raise awareness of this disease and hopefully to rally up some support.

My journey started when called to the breast screening unit 18/12/15. #Breastgate

Over the Christmas period I consciously decided to enjoy my time and prepare myself for what lay ahead.

My immediate friends and family have been amazingly supportive, along with my boss! I'm feeling optimistic and positive. So, fingers crossed it all goes to plan. Here's to the L&D team that are looking after me in the next few weeks.

Ladies! Check yourselves – so many women now stand a much better chance and mine is a moderate grade.

I'm extremely grateful for all the messages I've received today. It has lifted me no end and I can look back on these and feel more and more determined to get over this!

Thank you from the bottom of my heart!

12th February 2016

As I've made my breast cancer public, I'm posting this update. Ladies, be breast aware! The earlier the better.

1. My breast is clear of cancer and has healed well.
2. Grading of cancer cell remains the same – 2 (hormone positive only).
3. Sentinel lymph node biopsy showed a trace of micro cancer cells.

So, to err on the side of caution, my lymph nodes need to be removed. Possibly mid-March – however, that may be brought forward (one-hour operation).

All in all, I'm relieved with this news and still have a way to go! But getting there.

Thank you for the support, Denise

I wanted to become a CRUK Media Volunteer. I signed up for that and was contacted by the media liaison officer, who arranged for me to have a post on my Facebook page for World Cancer Day.

Here it is...

I worked with CRUK and went on several radio interviews, always seeing this as an opportunity to create awareness. #Hope

I was contacted by the NHS, CCG (clinical commissioning group of Luton) and asked to do a breast awareness screening video (https://www.youtube.com/watch?v=Y-isl0sCdfc).

Following on from this and after meeting a journalist from ITV Anglia News, we arranged some TV footage of me in a school, demonstrating and talking about breast cancer awareness (https://www.itv.com/news/anglia/2018-02-02/cancer-on-the-curriculum-one-womans-mission/).

I worked with charities to speak about my experience, and it started with me writing a talk for the CRUK Race for Life event, which was within a few weeks of me finishing radiotherapy.

From this, I went on to speak with various groups of women to spread that all-important message.

I took every opportunity I could for getting the all-important message out there!

Exercise

Back in July, 2015, I decided to do a 5K, CRUK Race for Life run. I decided to run at the St Albans venue; a great park with lovely views and jogging around the lake is very special. I was determined to complete the 5K, as I was doing a fundraiser and remembering loved ones. I managed to finish in thirty-seven minutes, and I recall thinking that's not bad, but for me, it was more about the cause and taking part, not the time.

Unbeknown to me… I had breast cancer!

So, sitting opposite Dr James – my breast oncologist surgeon – I recall her asking about my overall health and fitness. I remember saying, "Well, I can jog three miles and I do Pilates."

Dr James seemed pleased, and I answered all the other general questions. My weight and overall health were in reasonable shape. On hindsight, when I look back, I do believe that my baseline fitness helped me with my three operations and twenty-one days of radiotherapy. I healed well from my first operation.

I was very well cared for by the hospital at home nurses, along with family and friends. My progress seemed straightforward (thankfully).

I was keen to get back to jogging and Pilates again, but naturally I had to wait. The removal of seventeen lymph nodes from under my arm also prolonged my return to exercise; all in all, it was a matter of a couple of months.

I did my physio for my arm and my body seemed to repair well after the radiotherapy.

I'm absolutely convinced that my baseline fitness made a significant difference to my healing and helped with my emotional well-being too!

This all combined to having an integrated approach and I found it was beneficial.

Four days after finishing radiotherapy I did Race for Life, Dunstable Downs in May 2016.

I have done Race for Life most years! It's a humbling and inspiring event, whilst providing the comfort of remembering loved ones and sharing stories of hope!

CRUK are one of my chosen charities to voluntarily support, because they research all cancers and I'm hopeful that survival rates will keep getting better. Also, treatment will be kinder and more targeted, so the impact will have fewer side effects.

Here I am with Courtney Culverhouse – Senior Events Manager, CRUK.

So, I'm now seven years post Breast Cancer and I did the 10K Vitality Run in London for the Association of Breast Surgery (ABS) in May 2019.

Here I am at the CRUK Race for Life – St Albans, Hertfordshire in July 2017.

Dr Ruth James (left), me (middle) and Dr Kath Kirkpatrick (right side), fundraising for the L&D Breast Cancer Unit.

My Story...

"Hope will be somebody's guiding light."

Screening and Breast Cancer

How wrong was I? I must confess that earlier in the year of 2015 I had received breast screening reminders.

Now, of course I realise the importance of screening, but I was just so busy with work, family and socialising that I'd cancelled an appointment with a view to re-making it. Why worry?

Until this day…

Whilst sitting looking out the window of the office where I worked, I felt what I can only describe as an elongated vein in my left breast.

I remember thinking, *that's odd*, but I just put it down to hormonal changes and I also recall thinking, *I'll keep a check on that*. I'm certain that I would have checked my right one too just to make a comparison.

Fast forward to September 2015 and along with my partner, Pete, I spent a week on a very relaxing holiday in Menorca. Sun, sea, sand, chilling, and sangria… What more could a girl ask for?

However, I do remember being conscious of what I'd previously felt, and whilst sunbathing and chilling on the beach and relaxing by the swimming pool, I did keep checking and thinking to myself that next time I feel that… it may be gone.

I must admit it didn't spoil my holiday because I had pretty much convinced myself that it was something of nothing… particularly as I was perimenopausal. I had a lovely holiday and recall feeling very relaxed and revitalised on coming back home.

October came and went, so in November I remember having a phone conversation with my friend. As part of our conversation, I mentioned my lump and she said, "Denise, you've really got to go and get that checked out." So, with some encouragement from her, I contacted the breast screening unit and re-made an appointment (from my previous screening reminders).

I think at this point, it's important for me to highlight the importance of screening and how I took this service for granted and simply put it off! We all lead very busy lives and mine is no different to anyone else. So, this was a lesson for me to learn and I hope this encourages people to go for their screenings.

I received my date and went along for my first screening appointment, and I was informed that I would get the results by post.

About a fortnight later a letter landed on my hallway floor. After opening it, I immediately saw and read the return to hospital part for a recall to the breast screening unit.

I must admit that I felt an air of anxiousness, because the protruding vein/lump was still there, and I guessed it needed to be checked out further…

This was the first time that my worry started to kick in and the possibility that I had misinterpreted what the actual feeling was in my left breast after all.

Soon after that I called my friend and she said, "Don't worry, Denise, I think women get called back for various reasons, and it's probably a cyst or something. Isn't it great that you're getting thoroughly checked out?" She then said, "Look, I will come with you to the appointment."

So, the date came to return to the Breast Screening Unit of the L&D Hospital.

On arrival I checked in and was asked to change into a gown, so off to the changing cubicle I went with a basket for my clothes and bra. I'm sure getting into a straitjacket may have been easier than a hospital gown. Why back to front? And there are so many ties... It's so fiddly!

I probably made a joke about the gown to my friend... We've known each other a long time and the situation called for some humour, just to lighten the moment for a short while.

We both sat chatting in a side corridor – well, probably more me than my friend, who, I hasten to add, is a great listener – and I can recall looking up at the posters on the wall opposite where we were sitting. I also remember seeing a tea trolley with cups and saucers, biscuits, etc. It's funny how you can remember things about places.

Whilst sitting and waiting for my X-ray, I did feel slightly apprehensive about what was going to happen.

Then I heard, "Denise Coates," and a nurse escorted me to a room. I remember the lady; she was tall and serious looking... I didn't say a lot (which is rare for me, as I work in sales and talk for a living) but just let her get on with the job of taking the X-rays. She took a couple, and I was asked to go back outside to wait.

After waiting about five minutes, they called me back in and the lady did take some more X-rays and put a black mark on my chest (at this point, I did start to panic and wondered to myself, *what is that for?*). She then asked me to go back outside again and wait. I updated my friend, and I think she could see I was somewhat apprehensive and nervous. I did say, "Something isn't quite right." Then I was called into a different room and my friend was invited to come along with me.

I was introduced to a doctor and breast nurse, who said they would be taking care of me whilst investigating my breasts further. My X-ray pictures were pinned on the screen, but to be honest, I didn't take a lot of notice. She talked me through what they would be doing by using an ultrasound machine.

I laid on the bed next to the machine, and she examined my breasts first and then proceeded to use the ultrasound on me, applying the gel, then moving the probe over my chest back and forwards. During this process she could see an oval-looking image and told me it was a cyst that needed to be aspirated.

The nurse wiped on some local anaesthetic, and she popped the needle in… All the time I was watching on the screen… then by magic it disappeared… (*Was that just the problem?* I thought to myself, hoping it was). But then the doctor continued to look in the area where the cyst was and said to me that a biopsy from that area of my breast was required and a lymph node from under my arm.

Whilst this was all going on, I could see my friend out the corner of my eye, as she was sitting quite close by and could also see the screen… I think, like me, she was a bit concerned.

I got up and sat on the chair next to my friend and opposite was the lady doctor and the breast nurse. We sat waiting for a minute and she then looked at me and said, "Denise, there is an eighty per cent chance you have breast cancer." And at that point I remember looking up at the clock, thinking to myself, *oh my God, I'm up against this and that clock isn't stopping.* Although, for that moment in time, I wanted it to stop and just rewind to my life before finding out this dreadful news…

The doctor then informed me that I should go next door with the breast nurse to digest the news and she also said the hospital would send off the biopsy for examination and I would know within a week what the results were. She did say to me that sometimes they get it wrong, but she was certain that what she'd seen was indeed breast cancer.

We didn't stay very long with the nurse because at that point all I just wanted to do was get out of the hospital for a bit of fresh air. I remember looking at my friend straight into her eyes and just hugging her and saying, "Oh my God, I've got cancer." We both cried and she said, "Look, we will get through this, you've got lots of support. Let's wait and see what the results are." And with that I proceeded to drive myself back to work, where I told my boss what they had said.

At that moment in time my life started to change immeasurably.

Family and Friends...

Yes, You Have Cancer!

As I was waiting on the confirmed results of my biopsy tests, I thought to myself that perhaps I should only tell a few families and friends until I was certain about what type of cancer I had and whether my lymph nodes were infected, or what the actual state of play was with my prognosis.

My partner Pete was working up north and he was on his way driving home. As he'd asked me to let him know, I phoned him and relayed what I'd been told earlier that morning. I don't think it was a very long conversation; he needed time to digest it as well. All I really remember him saying was, "I'll be home soon."

My son Jamie, who was twenty-one at the time, bowled in from work as he does, like a freight train, and I spoke with him. His response was, "Mum, by this time next year, you'll be fine." I remember thinking, *do you know what, Jamie... that's good enough for me*. And I felt OK with him believing that himself! After all, breast cancer survival was getting better.

I asked my friend to pass on the (not-so-good) news to our other friends in the group, as we have all known each other since our early schooldays.

I telephoned my eldest brother Steve first and explained to him what I'd been told. I remember him being really encouraging on that first phone call and just saying if you need anything then please let us know, and I asked him to pass the news on to my sister-in-law Fliss and their family.

I called my other brother Robin and my younger sister Heather; it was difficult but something I felt needed to be done that day. Robin, like me, is outgoing and positive, and reassured me that cancer these days was treatable, and should I need anything, just ask.

Our youngest sister Heather was shocked, and a bit upset, so I reassured her, "Don't worry too much, until I know exactly what I'm dealing with."

They were all supportive... However, for my eldest sister Alison and her daughters, who lived in New Zealand, I decided to hold off until I had a more accurate prognosis.

In the meantime, the week passed quickly; after all, it was the week leading up to Christmas and we had planned to visit our family in St Agnes, Cornwall.

We were out Christmas shopping, and my mobile phone rang; it was an unknown number, and I felt a bit strange before answering it... Sure enough, it was the breast nurse from the screening unit to confirm my results. After confirming my details, she asked me, "Who are you with?"

I said, "I'm in the car going home with my partner."

She said to me, "Are you driving?"

I said, "No, my partner is…"

She then proceeded to confirm that I did indeed have breast cancer, but my lymph node biopsy didn't show any sign – phew! That was a relief.

She then proceeded to tell me that I would be seeing a surgeon within one week and my treatment plan would start.

That was it, then! I had breast cancer… What a wake-up call!

*

When I was alone with my thoughts, I tried to minimise the negative ones. I did consciously believe that remaining positive and forging ahead with this journey would mean staying steely and as healthy as I could possibly be. My emotional and physical body needed to be in reasonable shape to take this challenge on.

It was as though a light switched on and instinctively, I went into survival mode.

I viewed going to Cornwall for Christmas as a health tonic; after all, it's a beautiful place with breath-taking views and fresh air, along with the sea.

When we arrived in Cornwall with the family, I passed on the message to my brother-in-law and his wife, who were supportive, and I just said, "Look, I'm going to make the best of this time whilst we are here for a few days; try not to worry and let's enjoy Christmas as best as we can." I considered that these few days would be my break before I really knew what was happening and what I was up against.

It was a nice Christmas break, and my partner had also booked a health spa in Falmouth for me as a treat. So, with my sister-in-law and her friend, we headed off to Falmouth for the day. Part of my day was a massage treatment; I do remember mentioning this to the receptionist and they reassured me that it would be a light treatment. Whilst the lady was massaging me, I did feel a bit apprehensive, because I knew that somewhere were cancer cells, and would me having the massage affect anything? We had all the other benefits of going to the spa, along with a jacuzzi and sauna room, and afterwards we had a very nutritious dinner and just generally really chilled out with my sister-in-law Jo, admiring the beautiful scenery and sea views.

The few days flew by, and I guess I just parked the whole cancer thing in the back of my mind... but before we knew it, we were packing up and heading back to Dunstable, Bedfordshire where I live and kind of really preparing myself for what lay ahead.

Treatment Plan

A letter arrived on the hallway floor, the first of many... I could see it was from the hospital. It was a week later and post-Christmas. There was an air of anxiousness and uncertainty, but I was kind of pleased that this would be the start of getting better (fingers crossed).

I had no idea who I was going to see for my first appointment at the hospital – was it a lady surgeon or a man?

We arrived at the hospital, and it was a bit surreal finding our way to the cancer unit! I remember thinking, *why me! Why now!* as my life had plateaued into a level of balance, but hey... life isn't always like that, eh? And at this point, I still didn't know what type of cancer I had.

I checked in and sat waiting. I didn't feel ill, so that helped. I was with my partner, so I had some support and company.

Then I heard, "Denise Coates."

I turned to see a lady who showed me into a medical room, and she said, "The surgeon will be with you shortly."

While I was sitting waiting and taking some deep breaths, in walks a very petit lady who sat in front of me, along with a breast cancer nurse.

"My name is Dr James, and this is Jan, who will be your breast cancer nurse." Dr James asked if I was OK, and I expressed my concerns and feelings; her presence was really calming, and she spoke in such a gentle but factual way that I remember feeling instantly at ease.

Dr James then went through a series of general health questions, and I remember saying to her that I did 5K runs and Pilates... She seemed pleased with that. She then proceeded to tell me that I had invasive ductal carcinoma (*What a horrible name*, I thought to myself). She said it's hormone ER/PR positive cancer and was graded 2. My tumour was a moderate risk and about three centimetres.

However, on the upside, with no lymph node signs being infected and it being one of the common breast cancers, it was treatable. Phew! What a relief, but there was a journey ahead of me all the same.

Dr James talked me through my options and the treatment plan. First operation to remove a tumour from my left breast, and then a course of radiotherapy and adjuvant treatment of tamoxifen for five to ten years.

Due to my breast size and overall health, I could opt for a breast mammoplasty-style surgery, where she would remove the cancer and re-shape my breast.

It was a lot to take in, but by the end of the meeting I felt more optimistic about my prognosis. She was very endearing, and I instantly liked her (I felt very lucky to be in her care).

She also explained to me that a team of consultants and medical professionals combined would make up the overall care package and form the MDT (multi-disciplinary team), which was made up of a surgeon, radiologist, pathologist, oncologist, and breast cancer nurse – soon they became my 'dream team'.

She answered all my questions and reassured me as best as she could. She said, "We will schedule in your operation, and I'll see you then."

Dr James then passed me over to Jan, my dedicated breast care nurse, who explained the next steps and gave me a booklet that contained a lot of information about breast cancer and charity details, along with further support.

She said that I would receive a letter in the post for a pre-operative assessment and an MRI scan prior to my first operation to remove cancer from my breast.

Having more information about my prognosis, I felt ready to telephone my sister in New Zealand to tell her.

I hadn't had an MRI before, and I guess, like a lot of people, I was more concerned about the enclosed space, but how could I be frightened or complain? After all, I was being sorted to get better.

My pre-operation assessment day arrived, and I met a lovely nurse by the name of Di. I can honestly say that this was another day of feeling thankful for our NHS.

Sitting in front of this lovely lady, she looked down at her notes in a book! I thought, *Blimey, there's a lot of information there.* Then she proceeded to go through some family medical history. We could see the pattern of aneurisms, so Di scheduled an ultrasound test for that and my upper organs. I also had an X-ray prior to my first operation, blood tests, weight and height, checks, etc.

She said that I would get my results and my next visit to see the hospital was scheduled in.

It felt like I was in a relay team, and week by week, I was passing on the baton to either another test or medical meeting.

My last visit prior to my operation was for my MRI results.

Friday! Results day! Sitting and waiting with my partner in the cancer unit! The staff were running an hour behind, so time seemed to pass slowly, but I was fine with waiting, as I realised the importance of their time when sitting with others. When my name was called, Jan the breast cancer nurse said, "Sorry for the delay but we are getting a third opinion on your MRI scans and Dr James will be with you shortly."

I did panic a bit, because I couldn't figure out why three people were reviewing my images.

Dr James walked in with my images and proceeded to tell me that they suspected two small tumours behind the three-centimetre one. She also said there was something else behind the tumours but reassured me that she would remove this during my operation.

"So… the next time I will see you is on operation day; all dates and information will be posted."

Operation Day 4th February 2016

World Cancer Day!

So, with my bag all packed for my overnight stay at the hospital the next day, I headed off to bed, and before you knew it, I was awake and thinking, "Well, today's the day that cancer will leave part of my body; the irony, being World Cancer Day.

It was OK for me to have a drink, and I had some water with a small cup of coffee (but added a little bit of milk – ooops!).

Anyway, more about that later!

My partner and I headed to the hospital, and I checked in. It was about 7.30am and already there were quite a few people waiting…

My first appointment that morning was to head off to a radioactive area in the hospital to have some blue dye, which is called radioisotope, injected into my breast; this enabled the surgeon to locate my sentinel lymph whilst I was undergoing my operation.

I was informed that my operation was around mid-day, so we waited until I was called by Dr James.

We went into a room and had a quick chat. I mentioned that I'd had a small coffee with milk, and she said, "That may pose a problem with your anaesthesia, I'll check… There's a possibility that your operation will be rescheduled for the afternoon." I recall thinking how stupid I'd been, as black coffee or just water would have been fine. Anyway, Dr James proceeded to mark up my breast! I have to say during all this process I felt so relaxed, as it's done with such care and thoughtfulness.

She had a quick chat about the operation and then I went back outside to wait.

Not long after, I was then called by the anaesthesia doctor, who proceeded to tell me that indeed my operation was rescheduled and would be some time in the afternoon.

Whilst this was all going on, my partner was waiting and reading. He was waiting with me until I went into the operating theatre.

It was around 2pm and I was called into a side room to get prepared for my operation. I said bye to Pete, and I said, "I'll message you as soon as I can."

I changed into a gown and then was escorted to the top floor of the hospital where the operating theatres are. I recall walking down a long corridor looking out many windows on my way. A silly thought came into my mind about the programme *I'm a Celebrity… Get Me Out of Here!* My sense of humour was still intact.

I tried to help myself by taking some deep breaths steadily and thinking good thoughts and appreciating how lucky I was to be getting sorted out.

I sat waiting until a lovely tall man came and sat next to me and confirmed my details, asking a few questions whilst cross-checking a form. I remember saying to him that I was slightly uneasy, but he totally reassured me that it was his job to monitor me, and I was in very good hands, which I have to say, really reassured me.

We walked into the anaesthesia pre-operating room. I was asked to get on the bed. I noticed the double doors at the end… and the reality of what was going to happen really started to sink in…

The team in the room that day were good, and we chatted whilst they set about getting me ready and then administered the drugs to put me asleep.

And before you know it…

I could hear a voice saying, "Denise! You are now in the recovery room, and we are here with you." My eyes started to open further; I could see the clock, which showed it was about 5.30pm… I felt a bit sick and woozy!

I felt my left breast and shed a tear, as the thought of the cancer being removed was overwhelming! It felt compact and smaller! But… what a relief!

As I started to come around more, I asked the nurse for my phone so I could let my family and friends know that I was OK!

To mark the occasion, I took a selfie!

Once Pete knew that I was OK after my operation, he headed home.

I was in recovery longer than anticipated due to a shortage of beds on the ward and my friends were waiting for me.

By this time, it was about 9.00pm.

The porter took me to Ward 22 and just before entering the ward I was greeted by my friends. They stayed with me for a while, which was nice.

As I had made my breast cancer public for awareness reasons, I checked out the post which CRUK put on their Facebook page, with it being World Cancer Day.

Well, the number of well-wishers was amazing; people who didn't even know me were wishing me well. I was so lifted by this and receiving messages of hope.

I slept on and off through the night and was still feeling slightly overwhelmed that my cancer had gone! I was regularly being monitored for blood pressure and temperature, etc.

I awoke in the morning to a nurse pulling the curtains open around my hospital bed… and lo and behold, it was a lovely lady whom I knew! What a welcome surprise! Thanks, Deb.

There were usual comings and goings on a hospital ward, and I waited to see Dr James.

Dr James arrived with the surgical ward nurse to check on me and see how I was feeling. All seemed to be well, and I felt perky!

Later that day, I was able to go home and thereafter, for a week I was cared for by the hospital at home team, who called in every day to perform the routine checks and change my dressings, etc.

I had lots of lovely gifts and visitors. People were so kind! It was overwhelming! …I'll never forget it!

Friday was results day…

Before I knew it… the week had passed, and I was sitting in the waiting room of the breast cancer unit to hear about my results.

Keeping my fingers crossed, I got called into a medical room, where my dressing was removed by a nurse. I couldn't believe that the incisions had healed… I remember looking down on my breast. It looked a good shape. You could clearly still see a lot of bruising and it was swollen, but all in all, I was feeling OK!

The nurse asked me to wait for Dr James, who appeared minutes later with Jan, my breast cancer nurse.

Dr James checked the breast and then I listened tentatively for my results… The good news was that the margins were clear of cancer and the tumour biopsy was of a similarly grade as the original biopsy, so that was good.

Here was a curve ball…

Then, a little bit of not-so-good news.

My sentinel lymph node showed micro cells and based on that it was recommended that my lymph nodes were removed from under my left arm as a precaution.

I wasn't anticipating another surgery so soon after, but naturally, I went along with the medical advice I was given, and my second operation was scheduled for 23rd February 2016.

On the day of this surgery to remove seventeen lymph nodes from under my arm, I was operated on by the head of breast surgery, Dr Ravichandran.

I literally got to meet him in the pre-operating room, and I recall him standing beside me in his scrubs!

It reminded me of the programme ER. This is how our conversation went when he came to formally introduce himself:

"Sorry, I didn't get to meet you earlier, we've been so busy."

"That's OK, Doctor, I've read all about you on the internet!

"All good, I hope."

"Yes! By the way, will you sponsor me for Race for Life?"

"Yes!"

And sure enough, he did, along with my surgeon Dr James.

Don't Be So Hard on Yourself

When I was faced with my cancer challenge, the impact on so many areas of my life soon became apparent.

What about work? My family, my finances, bills, relationships, my household, and me?

My life?

On top of all these important and significant things in my life, I'm now faced with a life-threatening disease…!

I think that mums and carers who have that extra responsibility when they face a challenge themselves may find it difficult, but I do believe that reaching out for extra help, can make such a huge difference. It's hard for us to say no! but in all honesty, I really found that during this time, I had to put myself first before others.

So, here's a little bit about what helped me.

It's super important to seek the right support and help along with accepting that your life is temporarily now different than before. You will have the support of the medical team who are caring for you, but they are also caring for many others. I took it upon myself to search for cancer support groups and like-minded women, as they understood! We shared information and tips! How helpful is that?

For me the social media platforms where I came across groups of women were such a source of inspiration and sharing advice, supporting one another. Online, I met Dr Lisa Schwartz, from Los Angeles, USA, who was at the start of setting up an online self-help breast cancer support group. We could ask Lisa questions and she shared her knowledge base and expertise with us.

We even set up a Zoom meeting forum, so I was speaking with ladies from the USA and in the UK. I'm still friends with these wonderful women today! It really did help, as we shared our thoughts and feelings with one another, supporting each other the best we could.

The national leading charities will also provide support and rely on volunteers to support the work they do. Research is clearly the way forward for our future generations, and let's be honest, I'm here today because of it!

So, for me, support was key and led me on various paths of friendship, information, and self-help groups; it's made a big difference to my life.

You can adapt and still live your life through this process but having minimal stress and anxiety will really aid in your recovery – believe me, there's enough to contend with.

You may think this is easier said than done, but when your own life depends on you, it's a no brainier.

Take the help on offer! Should family and friends want to help you, let them! Go for walks in the park! If you can visit the seaside and take in the health benefits of the sea air and water, *go*! You will be so glad that you did!

I'm going to finish this chapter on where it begins… Don't be so hard on yourself. Why? Because it's a big challenge and the most important person is *you*! This is your life, and I believe that women are a source of support to so many and don't put themselves first!

This is your time to do that! Your mental and physical strength need it!

DON'T BE
SO HARD ON
YOURSELF

"Be the light and shine the way".

You are a *unique* and *beautiful* being.

Love you… You matter!

New Normal Life

Yep! My new normal life and giving one-person *hope*!

When I was going through treatment, I read a lot of articles and did my own Dr Google research on my cancer type! By the way, Dr Google hasn't done specific education, like a breast cancer team, particularly the surgeons, pathologists, oncologists, and radiologists.

I soon gave up on Dr Google, as the professionals have spent countless years learning their skill and knowledge base! They're the *real* doctors... not us or Google! And let's face it, nobody knows the histology of a human cell more than a pathologist or scientist.

Yes, I believe we can take some responsibility, but you are in good hands, and they know their stuff! Believe me!

I'd read an article on my way to Mount Vernon for radiotherapy – it was about the aftermath of cancer and the treatment, survival! Plus, your *new normal life*!

Mine all kicked in on my last day after the final blast of radiotherapy – I recall getting into the hospital taxi and looking back thinking, *Blimey! That's that!*

The weather that day was amazing! I remember looking up to the bright blue sunny sky with white fluffy clouds! Then gazing out the car window, looking at all the greenery and trees! It was as though I was looking at everything through a new set of eyes!

I couldn't stop smiling and feeling so grateful, *for my second chance at life!*

That day really was the start of my new normal life, with an overwhelming feeling of gratitude and a better understanding of humanity and kindness! There were simple acts of kindness, like being passed a cup of tea with a smiley face drawn on the lid!

I felt so proud of myself that day, so chuffed.
Was that it?
Had my cancer really gone?

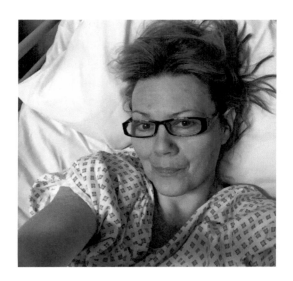

Yes... It had! Yeahhhhhh!

I was interviewed on BBC Three Counties Radio by Nick Coffer on Monday 3rd June 2019, along with Courtney Culverhouse of CRUK, who is a senior events manager and a breath of fresh air, promoting CRUK's Race for Life events!

Here is part of that conversation.

I felt recording this would remind me of why I have chosen to put myself in the public domain and spread the word about awareness of early detection of cancer and how giving hope can help others!

Nick Coffer

I remember you coming in a year ago and saying, "If I can be a beacon of hope to one person, then it's worth being here," and here you are again fifteen months further down the line, still being a beacon of hope to one person.

I cover cancer and life-limiting conditions and a manner of all life issues, and sometimes it can feel a bit *hopeless*! So, I like it when I have someone like you in, without – and I say this politely – without the drama, just someone who's been very poorly, who is doing well… That's also an important message, isn't it?

Denise

"Absolutely, and I had a conversation with Courtney before I came in and said, "That, for me, giving one person hope, was incredible." You know, three years ago when I was in my situation, and I was reading online and reading stories of hope! That consequently gave me hope! It really spurred me on! A glimmer of light in a dark situation.

I've embraced my new normal – don't get me wrong, it's a tough one when you get told you have cancer, and it isn't easy on yourself or your loved ones! But personally, I felt that getting on and having an integrated approach to life – healthy eating, exercise, looking after my emotional and mental health – really helped me.

I also found that associating myself with like-minded women who could share helpful tips and advice, especially breast cancer groups, further helped me through my journey. Some women have shared their tips too

Don't look back...

Move forward with excitement of what each day could bring.

Feel the earth beneath your feet and look up at the vibrant blue sky!

Keep being brilliant!

Survivor Stories

I think the most important part of every person's battle with cancer is mindset. My go-to quote through my treatment was, 'This too shall pass'. My diagnosis really opened my eyes to what and who really matter in my life. If things are going well, appreciate it, and if you are having a tough day, it's OK because this too shall pass.

I'm not sure how else to say it other than being diagnosis with cancer is a mind game. The waiting and not knowing was the worst. I think finding a tribe of like-minded women who are going through the same journey at some level was huge for me, because it is very hard to articulate how you are feeling when you don't understand it yourself. But strong women lift each other up and the amazing women I've met, including yourself, have done just that.

Karin Anderson
Ham Lake, Minnesota, USA

Breast cancer and cancer itself is a tough journey for all.

Each one different than the other, and some opposite from the other.

It's great to be able to share one's own experience because it's always helpful.

It helps another person go through their journey a little easier. I have been cancer-free for three years now. Every time someone sees me, they say that I look great, but the sad part is that I don't feel so great. Just because we are done with chemo, surgery, or radiation, doesn't mean that we are back to who we were before. In fact, we are different; we just saw our life flash right before our eyes. We slow down and take better care of our self. We become much more aware of what we eat and how we live our lives after cancer. We are much more grateful about life.

In the two years that I went through my journey, I learnt a lot from others that shared things that would help me. Sometimes we are not informed about what to expect, when it comes to the simple things, like how our skin and body is going to change, and products that we can use, because we can't use what we normally did before.

And now it's time for us to take charge and not let them make us feel that way anymore.

This is my version of the butterfly effect!

I call what we went through, or what you will be going through, metamorphosis, like what a butterfly goes through. We do chemo, lose all our hair, our breast and just want to crawl into a ball. We go into a cocoon, and as we complete treatment and surgeries, we start to transform into this new woman that we have become, because of this fight and battle that we've won. We change our look to 'pixie cut' and we all see things differently in life now, because of this horrible thing our body just went through. We start our transformation with our breast reconstruction, and our hair continues to grow, and we become this amazing, beautiful woman, stronger than before, and finally start to know the new face in that mirror, as we have no choice and start to come alive again. We become this beautiful strong woman, ready to take on anything!

Susan Gallagher
Sea Bright, New Jersey, USA

Have you ever had a time in your life when you felt like everything was in place? A time when you thought, *I am blessed and content. Life is good.*

Then *BAM*!

Out of nowhere, the rug is ripped right out from under you. Your life is turned upside down and inside out.

It could be illness, loss, financial crisis or simply unexpected change. Your spirits are crushed, hopes dashed, faith shaken.

Well, I've been there, and as I look back, I assure you: you will get through it, standing taller and feeling stronger.

Breast cancer was my *bam*, and it was a massive wake-up call.

Five years ago, when I was fifty-four, I was blindsided with a diagnosis of Stage II 'highly irregular ductal carcinoma' – a fast-growing tumour – in my right breast, a tumour that my initial mammogram did not detect.

Oh, I certainly did feel and was terrorised by a lump. Yet its irregular shape made its detection a challenge for professionals. It was only after receiving a standard letter saying that my mammogram was clear that I picked up the phone and requested further testing.

I knew something was not right. I acted on my intuition – something, I've learnt, that is often hard for women to do.

There is no 'good' type of breast cancer, yet the phrase 'triple negative' carries a heavy weight.

The disease is less understood than other types of breast cancer. Although triple negative breast cancer tends to have poorer survival rates than other types, this blunt statistic hides a slightly more optimistic situation.

Yes, there is a higher chance that the cancer will come back within five years. Yet once that hurdle is cleared, then the chances of survival are greater – something that rarely gets mentioned when people talk about this monster.

In a flash, I received an eye-opening crash course in the world of breast cancer research and treatments.

I decided to have a mastectomy and reconstruction – first on my right breast, then the left – then six months of chemotherapy.

My message to all survivors: once you've processed the shock and allowed yourself anger and a brief time to grieve, then reach out and trust others.

Get the information you need to choose what works for you.

Push past the fear and own the decisions you make to fight this beast.

One thing that helped me: I drank an organic tea – essiac tea, available at health food stores – throughout treatment, and I believe this helped ease nausea during treatment. I also kept up my routine of doing yoga and Pilates.

Today, I have passed the five-year survival mark — and I am ever-grateful to my oncologist, Dr Elisabeth McKeen, who has constantly cheered me on. Her compassion is a gift.

Other gifts were the lessons my cancer taught me: First, that the unexpected *bams* we experience can give new meaning to our lives.

Before I got breast cancer, control, discipline, and routine owned me. Things always had to be done and in order, at a frenzied pace. Today, I work on slowing down and taking my time to look at the landscape around me.

I'm learning to shed my need for control and place greater trust in letting things happen naturally.

Today, my life post-cancer is nothing short of panoramic. I am more open, more loving to myself, more vulnerable.

Think about it: when we are not completely comfortable with ourselves, we guard our insecurities and isolate our true selves.

When we are vulnerable, we experience true connection – respect for ourselves – and we then attract others who are inspired by our openness.

So, I encourage everyone to show your complexities. You will be pleasantly surprised.

More than anything else, cancer has strengthened my view and value of our human connection, and the significance of human kindness that means so much more than things. I now know that our human spirit can overcome and soar above adversity.

I am humbled to be healthy and alive today. This life is a gift; every day is a gift.

Our ability to achieve does not define us! It's our ability to love and be compassionate to others using whatever gifts God has given us that defines each of us. So, do what you can while focusing on what's important.

I'm now learning, with practise, to stop talking long enough to really hear what others have to say. When we invite others to share their fears and concerns – their story – we all benefit and feed off a renewed sense of mutual respect and enthusiasm.

My message today: find your life.

Embrace it. Own it. And live like crazy.

Sally Ann Nisberg
Palm Beach, Florida, USA

June 2015, I was diagnosed with grade 2 stage 2A DCIS, oestrogen, and progesterone positive. At the beginning I was afraid of the unknown, from diagnosis to treatments. During radiation it was stressful and lonely. I had one person who experienced breast cancer that I talked with, who calmed my fears of surgery and radiation treatments. I have never met her in person, just spoke with her on the phone a couple times. Later I came across a Facebook page a physician had set up during breast cancer awareness, and instantly I loved being part of a group with women who had the same diagnosis and knew what it was like. I was not alone, and I had access to this group twenty-four seven, and being that people all over the world were in this group, I had a person to talk to anytime. Most of the people were positive and helpful. Negative people just brought me down and I would skip over anything I did not want to read. Meeting with others on Zoom was great because it was more personalised; it was like being in each other's homes for a visit and chatting for an hour.

What helped me the most through my experience was having other women to talk to and share experiences. I am now a four-year survivor, and it has been inspiring to keep up with some from the group and cheer one another along, as our journey never ends at the completion of treatments.

If I had to share with what helped me the most, it would be support groups. Allow friends and family help with household affairs – I did not take time off work because I did not want to sit at home by myself, but I could take rest periods at work.

Having a person or group to talk to in person or even online groups was extremely helpful and helped me not feel alone.

Karen Oaks
Danville, Virginia, USA

For the men...

Nick is from the UK and here is his story...

My mother had breast cancer in the 80's so I was aware of it, and the possibility of it being passed down to male members of the family as well as female.

I wasn't doing a specialised check of myself but was aware of what felt like a fatty lump in my chest. Not painful, but odd. I visited a walk-in centre that day and was referred to my GP who I saw within a couple of days. I then went through the process of visiting the specialists at the local NHS hospital, culminating in a biopsy. This confirmed that it was indeed cancer, although the lump I had found was not!

The surgeon was very straightforward, which my wife and I appreciated, and strangely, rather than feel distress and upset, I was overcome with a feeling of fight!! "Let's do this" became the mantra.

I'd heard of facebook and support groups but found the best way for me to deal with it was to let only a very tight group of family and friends, and to keep it as much as possible to myself.

The surgery followed within a week or so, after which I was advised that the lump had been successfully removed, along with surrounding tissue, and several lymph nodes on the same side to check for spread. It was a few days later that I was told that there was no indication of further spread.

I have been advised that I have a mutated BRCA 2 gene, so am aware that this may, in turn be passed to my children. It is important that men are aware of the possibility of contracting this, and to keep vigilant.

I consider myself very fortunate to not have had to undergo

either radiotherapy of chemotherapy, but instead to just take a dose of tamoxifen every day. I am now 5 years post op and can withdraw from this medication.

Some words from Nicks partner…

I may be wrong, but I think the worst time was the waiting to find out if you did nor did not have cancer, we decided to get busy thinking of positive things, so we started to arrange our wedding which was wonderful to be thinking of a huge gathering of all our family and friends whatever the outcome. I also remember you being offered a 2nd mastectomy on the other side for cosmetic and peace of mind reasons which you had, but that you also were self-conscious of taking your top off on holiday by the pool. You had been offered but declined the tattoo nipple.

I also remember you saying (can't remember the time frame) when you were told you were now a survivor of cancer not a victim.

You decided to embrace your scar as something to be proud of and are going to have a big bird tattoo on your chest.

Finally, in July 2018 Nick shared this message on his social media platform.

So, a year ago today, I had a mastectomy (yes, blokes can have them too!). I had a lump confirmed as cancer, for which surgery was the only option. My mother died of breast cancer at the age of 44, so there was always a thought in my mind that this could happen. I found the lump by pure chance and within the space of a few days had undergone a biopsy which confirmed my worst fears! HOWEVER, The NHS, and the St. Albans breast care unit, have been nothing short of magnificent, guiding and supporting myself AND Karen through the whole process, including me having further 'risk reducing' mastectomy surgery on the other side, in March 2018.

Why am I posting this?

Andy why now?

It is true, that it's quite rare for guys to get breast cancer, but it CAN happen. So, for us men (and the husbands, brothers & sons etc of my Facebook friends) it's not just all about checking 'the twins'!! Make sure you have a good 'feel' around elsewhere too! Early diagnosis, like I was lucky enough to have...could save your life!

Survivors' Tips

The best tip I received was from my oncologist: *"Stay off the internet!"*

- Put yourself first. I know that is the hardest thing to do, and no, I didn't do it myself.
- When having radiation, take along the cream you will apply and do so before re-dressing.
- Listen to your body… If it's telling you to rest, rest. And don't feel bad about it!
- You are not alone.
- Take a trusted friend/family member with you to doctor's appointments and chemo, to take notes and be that second pair of ears!
- Breast cancer mostly affects woman. Many women prioritise their family and friends' need above their own. This is compounded if we are also in a helping profession (teacher, nurse, social worker), as many of us are.
- This is a time to prioritise yourself. Develop more self-awareness. Detox from dysfunctional relationships. Do less for others and more for yourself.

- *Denise, another one is to* listen *to your chemo nurse, especially on day one – she/he will be a wealth of information and coping hints.*
- *Let family and friends help you, don't be too proud to ask. Having a good support system is essential. And remember you are not alone. My husband was so supportive, I thank him to this day.*
- *Be informed, ask questions until you fully understand what all those doctors are telling you.*
- *Pretend you are in a sinking boat. Anyone who is in there bailing with you can stay, anyone who doesn't* must *be cut out while you are fighting this disease. You may be surprised at who that is: family, best friends, others who have gone through cancer. You can have them back when your treatment is done. Try not to take it personally – some people just can't look at their own mortality. Anyone who puts their needs before yours or wants your support to help them through* your *cancer* must *go. Find something good in every day. Sometimes that is the hardest part. Keep fighting.*
- *You're always told to be positive – really hard sometimes, so my sister said be positive twenty-three hours a day then take an hour each day to feel sorry for yourself – cry, scream, rant, whatever you must do – and boy that made all the difference in the world! Allow yourself to be scared, tired, resentful. Have all the emotions you need, if only for one hour a day and in private.*
- *Take all the help you can get!*
- *Buy button-up shirts and lots of cotton camisoles that you will throw away at the end of chemo and radiation.*

People have all kinds of suggestions. Just smile politely, when you can, and walk away. I was starting chemo, and someone was adamant that smoothies would cure me. I just put my husband on the phone to deal with her. I found so many great ideas on Facebook. Women who had gone through the same thing. Facebook is great, the good and the bad.

During radiation treatments I bought soft white men's T-shirts and jersey shirts to wear next to my skin at night and I wore them under my bra during the daytime.

1. *Buy some fleece or cut up a T-shirt. Use the fleece to wrap around the drains so they don't stick to your body.*
2. *Take pain meds on time. It is easier to catch the pain early rather than trying to use it once it is severe. My doctor compared it to having one cup of water… Would it work better when it starts to smoke or after the fires have started.*
3. *Save some pain meds for week three when the nerves begin to wake up.*

Painting my nails dark on certain types of chemotherapy stops them from falling off – a great tip if going onto docetaxel or paclitaxel.

Cancer and Mental Health

CBT

Having some prior knowledge about CBT (Cognitive Behaviour Therapy) before getting breast cancer was something I didn't really use; however, it was within days of being told 'you have cancer' that this talking therapy kicked in.

Emotional support is offered to cancer patients as is counselling and I think it's well worth considering but for me CBT has proved beneficial, and it's also assisted me with life in general.

Basically, I reframed my thoughts and switched them, so as an example, If I felt any negative words creeping in I would (in my mind) change that word into something more positive. For example, instead of telling myself, I can't sleep... I told myself. "Yes, you can sleep", and I kept practising changing the narrative around my thoughts.

I understood that reacting to the thoughts of fear may set of a chain reaction of chemicals that could have an impact on my physical wellbeing. I realised that being in a constant state of worry and anxiousness would be harmful, so doing CBT was my way of overcoming that.

For me It's still an on-going learning process and I find myself checking in on this therapy as I do believe it really helped me.

Cognitive behavioural therapy (CBT) can help you make sense of overwhelming problems by breaking them down into smaller parts.

In CBT, problems are broken down into five main areas:
- situations
- thoughts
- emotions
- physical feelings
- actions

CBT is based on the concept of these five areas being interconnected and affecting each other. For example, your thoughts about a certain situation can often affect how you feel both physically and emotionally, as well as how you act in response.

https://www.nhs.uk/conditions/cognitive-behavioural-therapy-cbt/how-it-works/

Train your thoughts to have good outcomes and breath deeply. This way your body will stay healthy and strong. You will become happier and feel more secure in yourself.

Go on...try it!

Research and Hope

I can't highlight this enough.

When I was reading stories about survival, it gave me so much hope!

When I was faced with this difficult challenge, having hope and a determined mindset enabled me to work through the challenge step by step.

Also, the insights into CBT and NLP I believe really helped me, coupled, of course, with medical intervention. I did take some responsibility for my own health too by trying to eat and exercise. I found that Pilates and jogging gave me a sense of joy, and another big impact was appreciating the simple things in life, like a walk in the park!

Naturally I've learnt a little bit about cancer and the work that the scientists do. I understand that moving forward research is key and is vital for future treatment plans. I totally advocate and support research, particularly as they discover less harmful ways of treating cancer.

So many lives and families are affected by this dreadful disease. We probably all know somebody or a family member that has had it. So, it really is in the hands of the professionals for our future generations to benefit from. I hope that they continue to find innovative new treatments and then more different types of cancer can improve on their survival rates. I'm aware that breast cancer survival particularly some types of breast cancer are easier to treat than others. I've always been keen to do the work that I've done and to shout about awareness, because hopefully it will help women of the future.

Andrew Selous MP says, "The golden key to cancer is early detection," and I couldn't agree more.

Why did I campaign?

Well, learning that children had limited teachings and considering our current times, I thought that making a stand now would help them in the future! Their knowledge and mental health are paramount for a good society moving forward.

My meaning of HOPE
- Happiness
- Optimism
- Persistence
- Empowering

I hope that somewhere in this book you find some guidance and it helps. I had to follow my instincts as well as ride on the crest of this wave, but on the night of my first operation when I was inundated with messages of hope it meant the world to me. Thank you!

Take a moment to

Look up at the vibrant blue sky.

Smell the freshly cut green grass.

Stare at the trees proudly standing firmly in their roots, fixed and tall…

Just like me,
You too can
Stand Up to *Cancer*.

Recurrence

Deal with what you know and recurrence?

When I sat with the oncologist who was part of the MDT team, he explained to me what my survival rates were and demonstrated this by using the NHS predict software – which captures your data based on your cancer type and other crucial factors. He talked me through this information and my chart showed that I had an eighty-five per cent chance of surviving for ten years.

My treatment was made up of mainly surgery and adjuvant was radiotherapy and a hormone receptor blocking tablet, commonly known as tamoxifen. I was offered chemotherapy, as there had been some micro cells in my sentinel lymph node, but not in the seventeen that were removed from under my left arm. The oncologist said that I was in 'No Man's Land', and in line with hospital treatment protocol, he had to offer me chemotherapy, but it was my 'choice' whether to have it or not! I do recall him saying that if one more lymph node had been infected, there wouldn't have been a choice! Based on the five per cent extra protection, I decided against it.

I recall looking at the graph and feeling relieved that I had an eighty-five per cent chance of surviving for ten years.

I think it's fair to say that most people who go through the cancer journey come out and have some thoughts about recurrence.

For me it became more apparent after the treatment. I learnt more about cancer and understood that unfortunately it can come back not only in the primary area but others as well.

Since having my breast cancer, I was under the hospital's care for five years, and so I felt a level of protection really. Because my whole outlook on life had changed, I knew that I needed to make the best of every day and most of the situations that I found myself in.

For me the support groups have been great for sharing information with like-minded women and having the opportunity to ask questions, some around recurrence. It provides a sense of comfort and support… putting a question out there and reading several responses and encouragement really helped me. On this occasion, I did post a question and received some positive feedback from women.

I just took what I felt was the best piece of information and it really helped!

All in all, and with the help of visualisation techniques, I believe I had packed thoughts of recurrence into a box and parked them in my subconscious mind.

Until… my fourth mammogram, I was sent a recall letter and for some reason I had a feeling that might happen. I didn't get the OK letter, and after waiting for two weeks, I sent my breast cancer nurse Jan a WhatsApp message and asked her to check for me… Later that day she called and said, "There is a slight problem – try not to worry, but you need to go back to the hospital to the screening department for the following week."

I have already mentioned how CBT had helped me consciously think of controlling my thought patterns.

Suffice to say, I did look up information and ask questions within the breast cancer support group about recalls.

But in the main I talked myself into dealing with the problem (if there was one) on the day!

I was reading some recall posts on the charity sites, and one really stood out for me: a lady had been passed on some advice from a Macmillan nurse, who said, "Deal with what you know."

I kept repeating this over and over in my mind and got on with my days leading up to the hospital visit.

Fortunately for me, on the day of my recall screening, I had my mammogram done again by a radiographer. About three or four images were taken and I sat outside and waited with my friend.

"Denise Coates!"

Here goes... I was called in and sat next to a lovely lady doctor and a breast nurse. The doctor proceeded to show me the images on the screen and explained the two sets of images – one from a fortnight before and the ones on the day!

This time I wanted to fully see and understand my images and breasts on the screen, and I soon noticed that what was on the left-hand side, wasn't on the right set – there was a tiny white area at the bottom of my left breast, and on the right one I could see there was nothing.

The doctor then proceeded to tell me I was called back because of little white area and pointed to it!

Then she showed me the other set, which were clear! She thought that on that day of my mammogram it may have been some folded breast tissue, so that was a relief – phew! I said to her, "Are you telling me I'm, OK?" and she said, "Yes, but we still have to do a physical examination," and with that she proceeded to check me out and then used the ultrasound machine to make sure that everything was as it should be. After the ultrasound examination, she said that my breasts looked fine.

Yippee!

All in all, this experience has giving me more than taken away: firstly, it has made me feel more compassionate and have more empathy for others; it's also helped me to appreciate and feel gratitude and not to take life for granted.

In the aftermath of this journey, I've learnt more about myself and how I can help others. So many things have come to light since this happened, particularly learning about less fortunate women.

Through Dr James and her work with the Association of Breast Surgery I learnt that in Sub-Saharan Africa only thirty to forty per cent of women survive breast cancer! The very thought of this is heart-wrenching! So, helping them, and on a local level, has been a wonderful experience.

I hope in the future I can continue to speak about my breast cancer challenge and provide some insights for others and pass on my experience and even if it helps one person, then that's good enough for me.

Giving Back

Whilst I sat in Mount Vernon Hospital having radiotherapy treatment on the one hand, I witnessed the devastating effects of cancer and on the other, I saw humility and kindness beyond measure; it was here that I decided to volunteer my time when treatment was finished.

I was so overwhelmed with the care I'd received that all I wanted to do was utilise my skills for the charity sector! So, when I returned to work, I decided to dedicate a day per week to charity.

For a period of time, I became a voluntary fundraiser for the L&D Breast Cancer Unit This was my first insight into charity work, and with their help I gained some fundraising experience.

I also became and still am a CRUK Media Volunteer, I also voluntary fundraise for ABS (Association of Breast Surgery) raising funds for an international project in South Matabeleland, Zimbabwe with Dr Ruth James.

My biggest wish was to share my story in the hope it will help someone or a member of their family.

I have worked with several organisations and mainly with Challney High School for Girls. Having the opportunity to visit and speak about awareness and 'thank' them for their amazing fundraising which they do year on year with the Race for Life Day in October.

One thing that I'm passionate about is thanking volunteers too! They give their time to good causes and I'm sure it benefits both the volunteer and charity.

Here I am, at the opening of a CRUK Dunstable Superstore – October 2018.

I personally thanked the volunteers as they have all contributed to the charity's goals and the time they freely give helps towards people with cancer and research.

Giving back is meaningful and rewarding, it's shown me how generous people can be and the amazing things they do for others and that's a great feeling.

Thank you to ALL volunteers!

ABS

International Projects Fundraising

The Association of Breast Surgery (ABS) is the specialist organisation for healthcare professionals caring for any person with a breast problem. The association's membership includes surgeons and nurse specialists, as well as other members of the wider breast care team, all of whom have expertise in the assessment and management of breast cancer. The aim of the association is to promote the highest standards of breast surgical

care through research, training and education, guidelines, and audit.

ABS has recently developed an international network of members with the aim of improving breast cancer care in lower– and middle-income countries, with an initial focus on sub-Saharan Africa. The incidence of breast cancer is rising in Africa. African women are far more likely to die of their disease than women in developed countries. A woman diagnosed with breast cancer in the USA has a greater than eighty per cent chance of surviving for five years compared to only thirty-two per cent in sub-Saharan Africa. There are many different factors contributing to poor outcomes for African women, one of which is the lack of breast specialist knowledge and training.

The international network at ABS aims to collaborate with host hospitals in sub-Saharan Africa to develop teaching programs emphasising achievable quality standards in the diagnosis and treatment of breast cancer. The first team of surgeons and nurses travelled to Bulawayo in July of 2019. They had excellent feedback from the doctors and nurses attending the course and made many contacts for further collaboration. A second group delivered a three-day training programme in Nairobi alongside local clinicians and a team from the USA, and there are plans for a further programme in Uganda in 2020. Charitable funds can be used to supply basic equipment such as core biopsy guns and needles for workshops. This equipment can then be retained by the hosts for future use. The international network also funds places for surgeons from lower– and middle-income countries to travel to the UK for conferences, training opportunities and attend courses.

https://associationofbreastsurgery.org.uk/

*Gratitude is
at the heart of everything I do.
It creates my peacefulness and contentment.
I hope you feel the warmth it brings too!*

Awareness and Education

Let's get together and make a difference.

My breast cancer challenge was life-changing, and it's set me on a course of self-discovery like no other, using my conscious mind to make the changes necessary to survive. Seeing first-hand the devastating effects really pulled on my heart strings and gave me a wake-up call to humility and kindness.

I'm passionate about our future generations understanding how prevention and awareness will save not only their lives, but that of their families too!

I learnt that cancer awareness wasn't taught in schools, so I made it my mission to try and do something about that. I visited my local MP and he helped me along with leading charities to introduce health prevention and awareness into PSHE which forms part of the school curriculum.

Spreading awareness and early detection of cancer, was the golden key, as quoted by the Right Honourable MP for Southwest Bedfordshire, Andrew Selous.

With my media experience, I set about speaking to our local ITV Anglia News journalists, and Challney High School for Girls, agreed for me to be filmed demonstrating a mini test breast to get that all-important message out there!

Cancer on the curriculum – one woman's mission.

https://www.itv.com/news/anglia/2018-02-02/cancer-on-the-curriculum-one-womans-mission

Photo's courtesy of ITV Anglia News.

With the approval of the school, I talked with the girls and demonstrated a mini test breast. This is what Rhoda, aged fifteen, had to say:

As a representative of my school council at Challney High School for Girls, I had the amazing opportunity to receive an eye-opening talk from Denise. She raised our awareness on a subject that many of us would think we know about, but in reality, we don't. And that is breast cancer.

She shared with us her journey. A journey full of ups and downs. A journey of challenges, but she proved to us all that it is possible to come out as a winner, and that can be many more people.

Denise brought in a plastic mini demo sample breast which contained a lump, and it was astonishing to know many women out there somewhere in the world may be living with one and don't know. This made me reflect.

When I'm older, I would like to study medicine to eventually become a doctor, and like I once said, "Now I know, and maybe one day I'll be able to save a life!"

For a year, I became a charity ambassador for the NHS Luton and Dunstable hospital and

part of my voluntary work was to speak about the hospital and the good work they do in the community.

Going that extra mile and being supported by an MP has been a good experience for me. Again, people with good intentions really stand out! I met him; he said we were a good 'team', and I would agree! Thank you, Andrew.

Fast forward September 2020, prevention and awareness have been included in the national curriculum. I'm so relieved and grateful for the help I've received and with this knowledge, I hope more cancers are caught early. Meeting the criteria of teaching and it being delivered in a constructive way will save so many lives!

I'm so happy about that! Thanks to this school and these girls!

My immense gratitude goes to Nic Ponsonby, Liz Summers and Andrew Selous! And I'm so, so proud of the girls at Challney High School for Girls.

Contributing towards equipment for the L&D Breast Cancer Unit, which will help women in our local community!

Challney Girls School Visit

l. How did you find my initial approach and working with me to reaching your objectives for Race for Life?

From the first day when you popped in just to chat, I could see your passion for what you wanted to do. I liked your confident and friendly approach, and enthusiasm about wanting to make a difference to others, both battling with and raising awareness of cancer. The students in school were delighted to have you there for the day and loved that you joined in. Many could not believe that you did this five times! With regards to reaching the objectives, this is the best total ever and I truly believe that you are joining us for every year group assembly put things in perspective for some of the students and encouraged them to fundraise even more.

2. How did the children benefit from meeting me and the message I delivered?

I think having someone local and having fought and battled cancer themselves had an impact. I also think that the message you gave them about checking and encouraging family members to check was inspiring. I think given that the students and their families use the Luton and Dunstable themselves, this helped to put things into context for them. I know that they were chuffed when you asked them if you could join them on the day too. I guess it is not often that our students get to meet a cancer survivor.

3. What was the overall feedback from your headteacher and fellow staff members?

The staff all commented on how lovely it was of you to join each year group and to personally address each of the year groups. They liked the personal touch, and many said that it was nice that it was not an upsetting message, but raising awareness for others, while giving something back to the community

4. What was the overall feedback from your students?

Students loved the talk and some even shed a little tear, in a nice way! Students said it motivated them and that it was great to have Denise with them all day. They thought Denise was very nice and passionate about helping other people, so this gave them the motivation to raise as much money as possible.

5. Following on, would you recommend a workshop to cover cancer awareness by using factual methods identifying the markers for potential problems?

I would recommend a workshop to raise awareness of cancer and I feel that something that would really benefit students would be to focus on things like breast cancer. The reason I say this is that

I know that many females do not actually know how to check, or what a lump feels like. This would be of benefit to all students.

Nicola Ponsonby – Assistant Headteacher (Pastoral and Guidance)
Challney High School for Girls

My Talk at Dunstable Downs

My breast cancer experience

"*Denise, there is an eighty per cent chance you have breast cancer.*" *For me it was like…* OK, what's next?

Briefly a feeling of vulnerability set in, but my conscious mind soon kicked into action. I rolled up my sleeves and said to myself, Denise you can do this! *My mindset and actions were steadfast, and on reflection I could see this helped not only me but also the people supporting me.*

Before you know it, you're at the starting line of the biggest race of your life! With sheer grit, determination and a positive mental attitude, unprecedented support from my friends, family, and work colleagues… I started my race against time!

I described my breast cancer journey like being in a relay, each 100 metres passing on the baton to the next leg of the race of tests, meetings, surgery, more surgery, results, radiotherapy, and hormone receptor blocking tablets.

A few curve balls thrown in too… Thank you, cancer!

Did you know that early detection of breast cancer – in fact, all cancers – give you a much better chance?

Women, *check yourselves… Go for your routine mammograms… the sooner the better!*

I'm going to emphasise the word 'TEAM' – the multi-disciplinary team of medical staff that looked after me! A breast care nurse, radiologist, surgeons, oncologist, and pathologist!

Let's not forget the ward nurses! Yes… they also fight your fight!

Apparently, from now on I will be living a 'new' normal life – one that I'm very grateful for! One that I will strive for, and one that I will continue to help CRUK for.

What cancer research means to me is… Cure, absolutely! Eradicate eventually and never return!

Good riddance to cancer… that's what I say…!

Thank you, each one of you! Let's come together and keep up the fight against cancer!

And finally, I wish you all the best for the future and I hope you thrive beyond your wildest dreams.

Be well.

Denise